M000020153

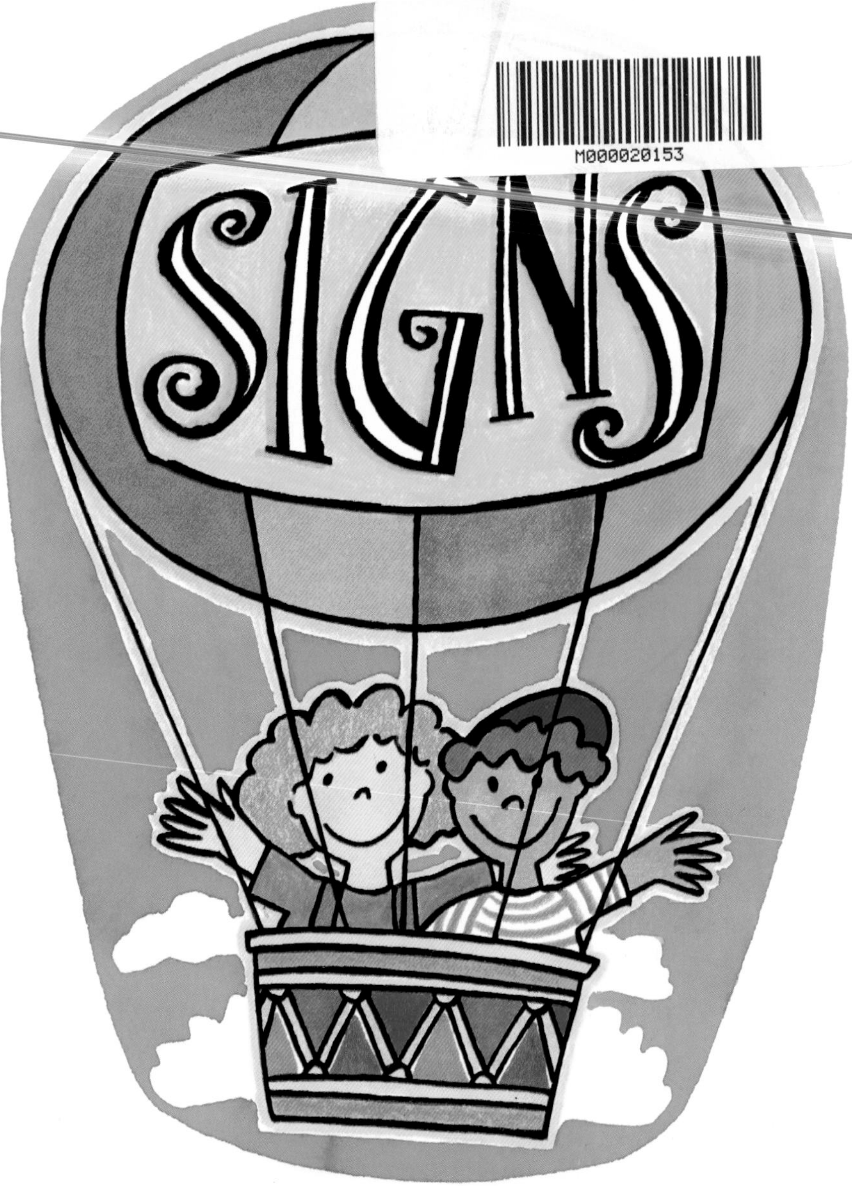

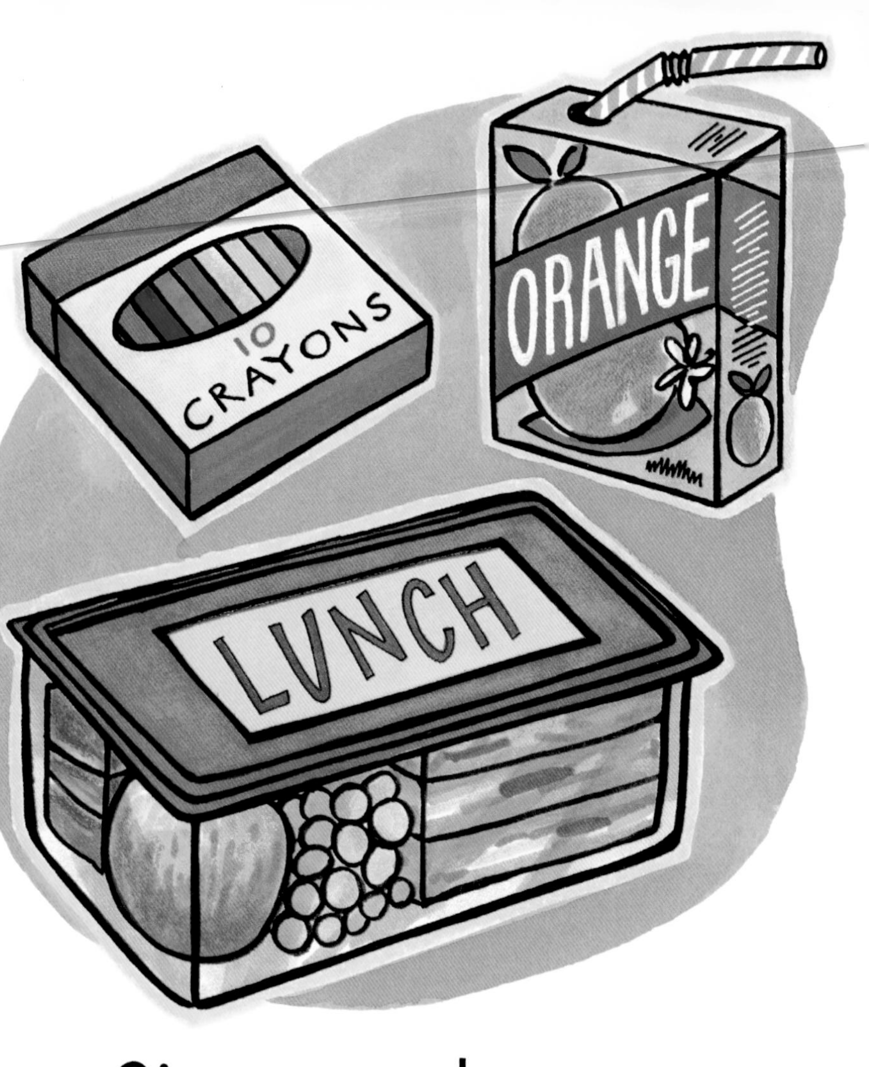

Signs on boxes,

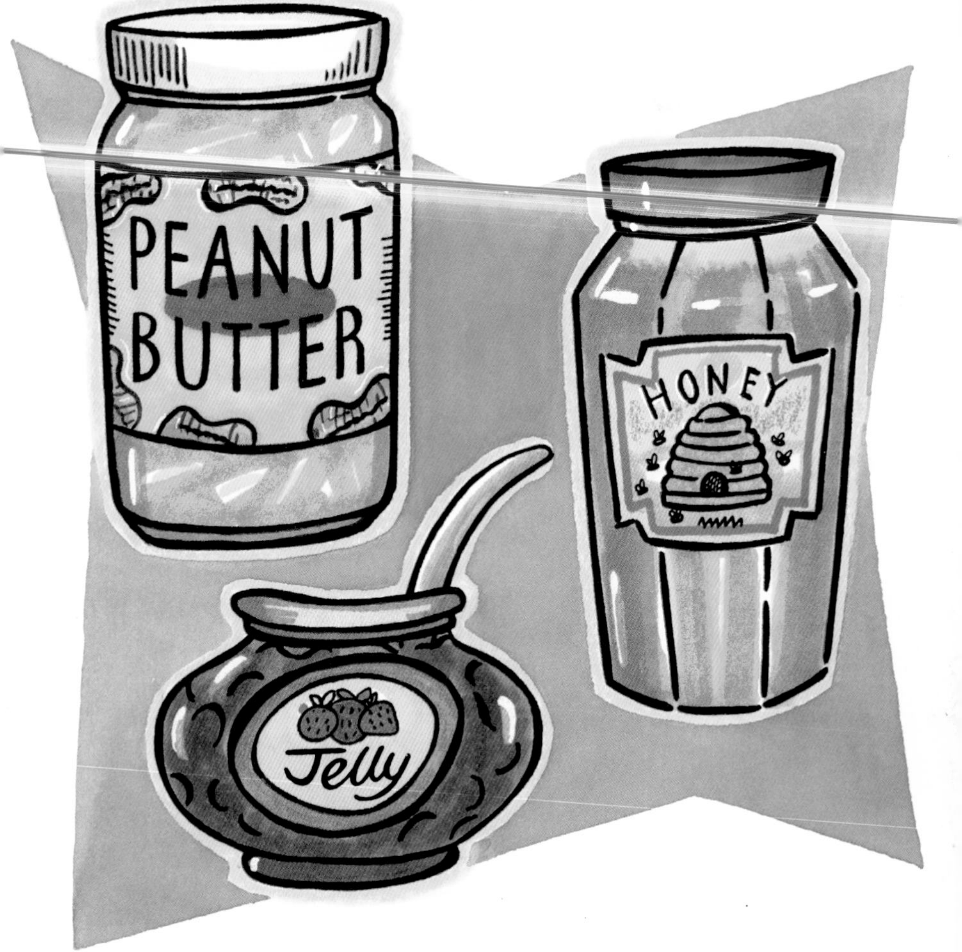

signs on jars,

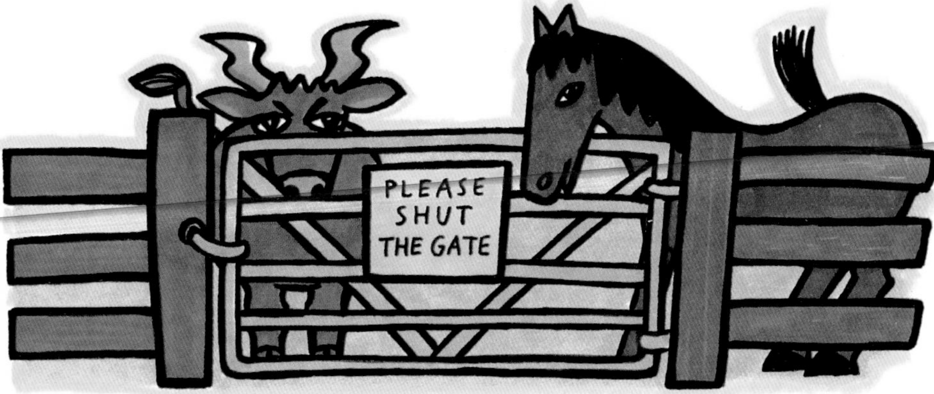

signs on gates,

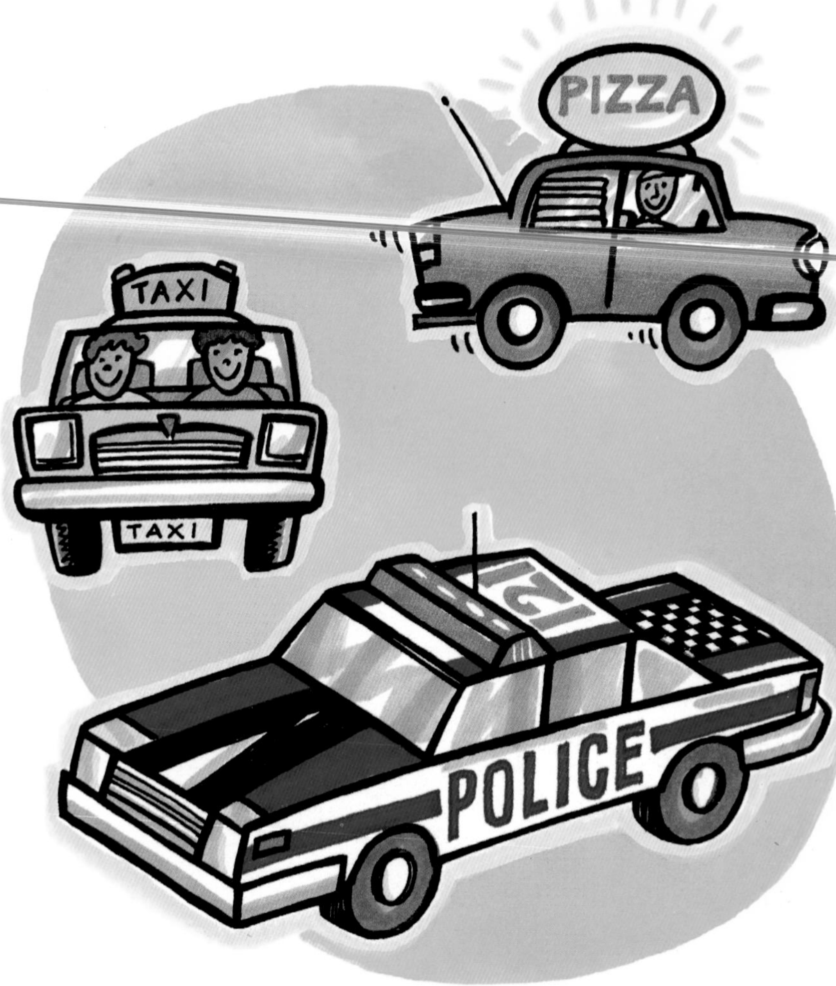

signs on cars,

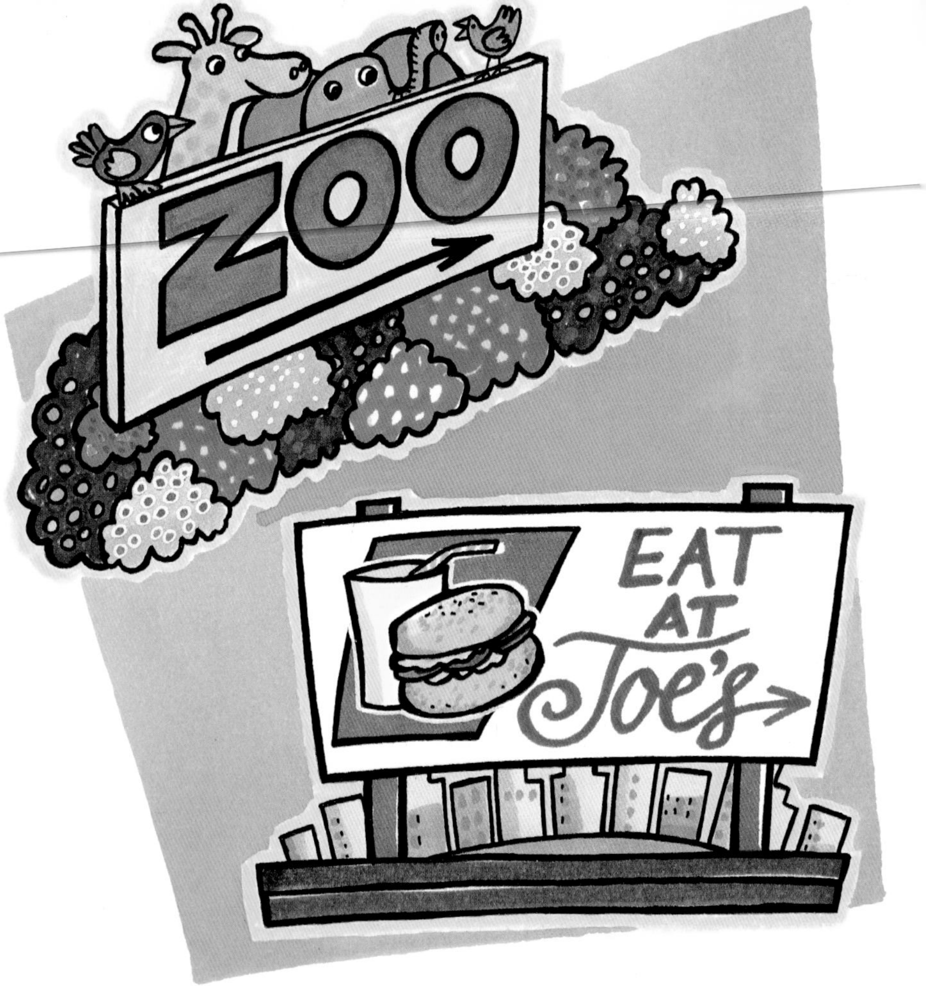

signs on billboards,

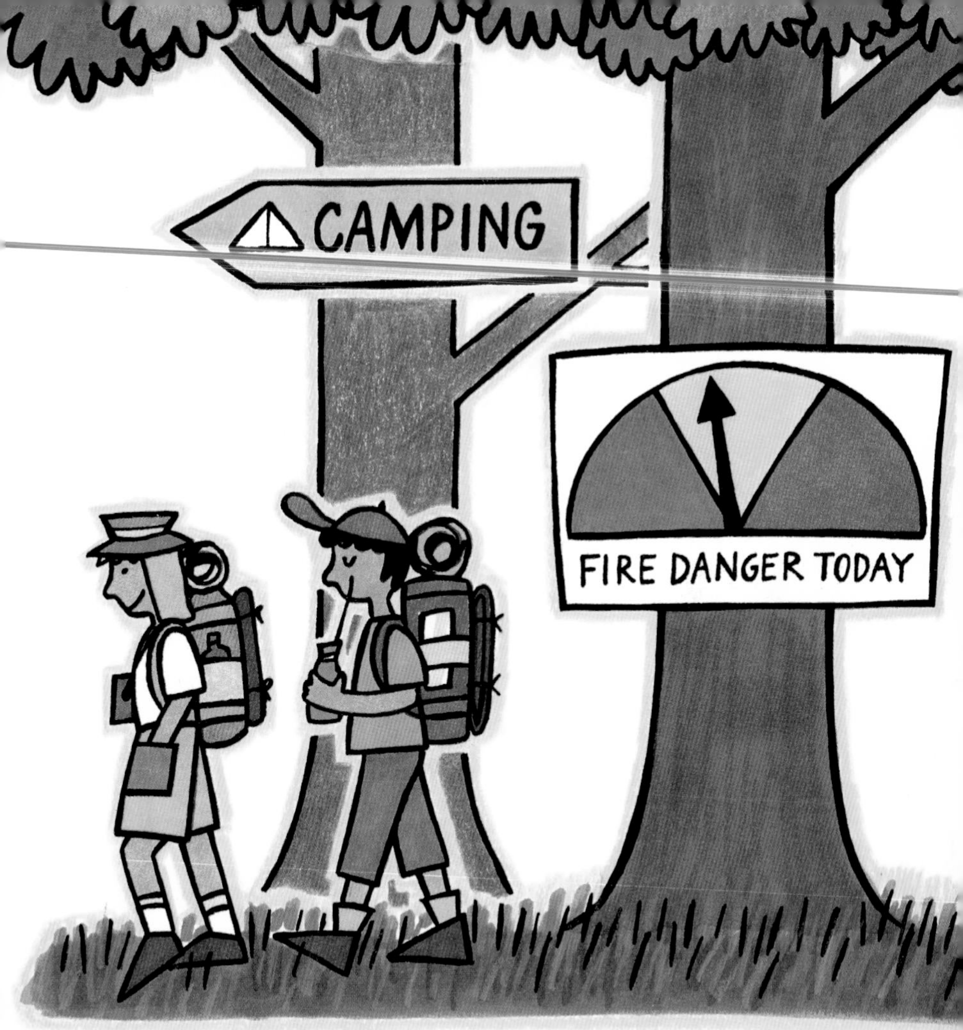

signs on trees,

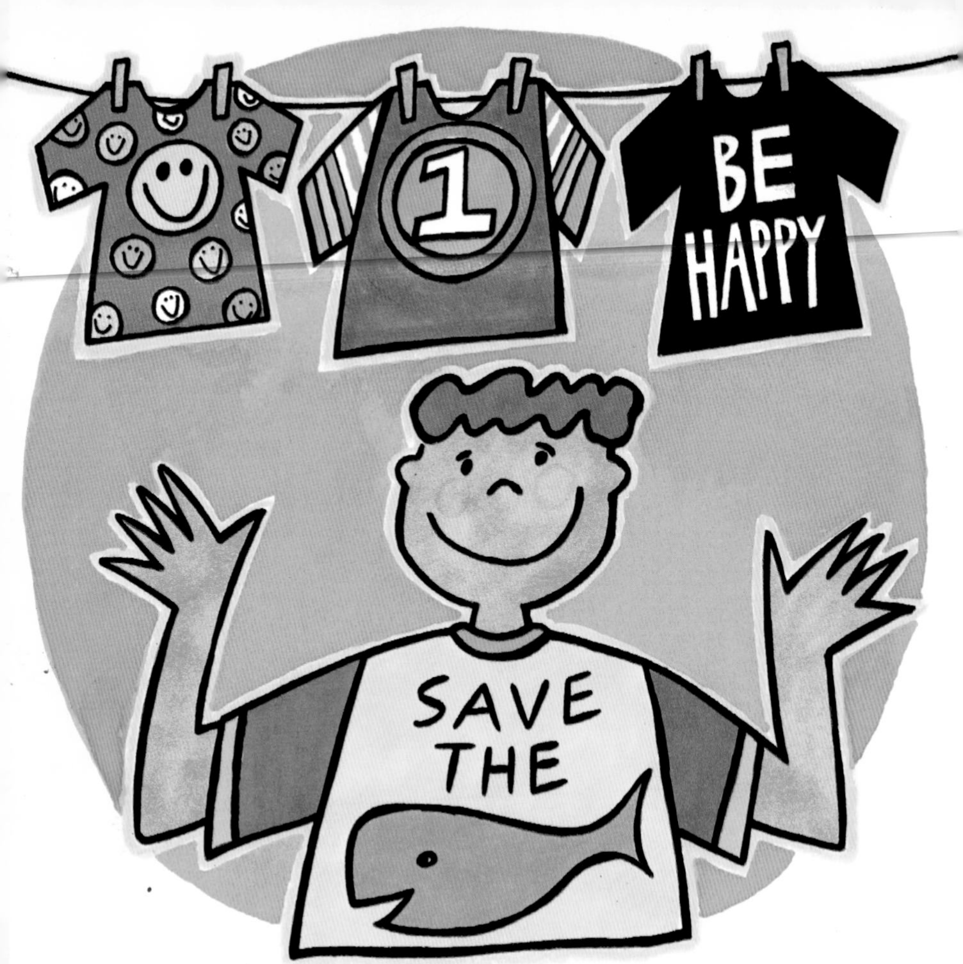

signs on t-shirts,
signs on me.